The Day
Animals Talked

Scripts and Poems for Reading Aloud

compiled by John Foster

Oxford University Press 1993

Oxford University Press, Walton Street, Oxford OX2 6DP

Oxford New York Toronto
Delhi Bombay Calcutta Madras Karachi
Petaling Jaya Singapore Hong Kong Tokyo
Nairobi Dar es Salaam Cape Town
Melbourne Auckland

and associate companies in
Berlin Ibadan

Oxford is a trade mark of Oxford University Press

This collection © John Foster 1993
Published by Oxford University Press 1993

A CIP catalogue record for this book is available from the British Library.

ISBN 0 19 916553 X

Typeset by Pentacor PLC, High Wycombe
Printed and bound in Hong Kong

Contents

The Behaviour Report

Tony Bradman

Good morning.
Here is
The Behaviour Report.

There's been some
Overnight sulking
In the small bedroom
After a telling off.
This could lead
To some scattered
Outbreaks of bad temper,
Squalls of tears,
And flouncing up the
Stairs during the day.
Later, there may be
A depression with some
Naughtiness at school.
This will be accompanied
By fog in the brain
While in class.

During the afternoon,
The baby will experience
Several damp patches
Which could lead to changes
And unsettled parents.

Later, two warm fronts may
Meet by the television.
This could cause a severe
Argument and a telling off
Before tea time, unless
Wind in the dining room
Causes gales of laughter.

And the long-term forecast?
There will be continued
Behaviour of all sorts.

Stay tuned . . . .
For further reports.

Well, What Happened?

Brian Moses

A poem for two voices

'I raised my voice,
he raised his fist.
I called him names,
he twisted my wrist.'

*'I held his arm,
he kicked my shin.
I said I'd get mad
if he didn't pack it in.'*

'He pulled my nose,
I belted his ear.
He said you'd better
get out of here.'

6

'I told him my brother
would give him a clout.
He said his big sister
would sort me out.'

'We argued and fought,
we shouted and swore.
I told him my dad
would give him what for.'

'We rolled on the ground,
we clinched and we kicked,
till someone said, watch it,
you'll both be nicked.'

'And that's when you came sir
and pulled us away,
but we're friends now, aren't we?
We've stood here all play.'

My Dad, Your Dad

Kit Wright

A poem for two voices

My dad's fatter than your dad,
Yes, my dad's fatter than yours:
If he eats any more he won't fit in the house,
He'll have to live out of doors.

Yes, but my dad's balder than your dad,
My dad's balder, OK,
He's only got two hairs left on his head
And both are turning grey.

Ah, but my dad's thicker than your dad,
My dad's thicker, all right.
He has to look at his watch to see
If it's noon or the middle of the night.

Yes, but my dad's more boring than your dad.
If he ever starts counting sheep
When he can't get to sleep at night, he finds
It's the sheep that go to sleep.

But my dad doesn't mind your dad.
Mine quite likes yours too.
I suppose they don't always think much of US!
That's true, I suppose, that's true.

8

Sunny Market Song

James Berry

A poem for three voices

1st Voice represents general market voices
2nd Voice, girl buying spices and seasoning from
3rd Voice, stallholder, who could be voiced by audience

1st Voice   Coffee
Spiced chocolate
Ackee

White yam
Yellow yam
Juicy melon

Breadfruit
Grapefruit
Arrowroot

2nd Voice   I want some cinnamon and tamarind, mam

3rd Voice   Buy quatty wo't' noh, gal—
Buy quatty wo't'

(*Fowls cackle*)

1st Voice   Tapioca
Sarsaparilla
Cassava

Snapper fish
Fresh fish
Strong charcoal

Dry coconuts
Water coconuts
Mango

2nd Voice   I want some cloves and lemon, mam

3rd Voice   Buy quatty wo't' noh, gal—
Buy quatty wo't'

(*A pig squeals*)

1st Voice   Custard apple
Ripe pineapple
Sweet potatoes

Cho-cho
Callalu
Coco

Soursop
Sweetsop
Sorrel

2nd Voice   I want some nutmeg and ginger, mam

3rd Voice   Buy quatty wo't' noh, gal—
Buy quatty wo't'

(*A goat bleats*)

11

1st Voice	Foo-foo plantain
	Ripe plantain
	Papaw
	Fever grass
	Strong-back herb
	Mount'n honey comb
	Orange
	Cabbage
	Hominy corn
2nd Voice	I want some allspice and pepper, mam
3rd Voice	Buy quatty wo't' noh, gal—
	Buy quatty wo't'

(*Dogs bark*)

1st Voice	Fresh whelks
	Beeswax
	Floor dye
	Blackeye peas
	Congo peas
	Okra
	Jackass rope
	Raw sugar
	Ripe bananas
2nd Voice	I want some scallion and annatto, mam
3rd Voice	Buy quatty wo't' noh, gal—
	Buy quatty wo't'

(*A donkey brays*)

Quatty is a Jamaican word for penny-half-penny.
Jackass rope is the slang term used for leaves of locally grown
tobacco twisted into the form of a long rope, coiled for
handling.

Christmas Present

Irene Yates

A play with three characters and many noises

Child
Narrator
Gran
Group for noises:

Television	
Cat	Milkman
Christmas tree	Grandad
Dog	Brother
Doorbell	Mum

Narrator   I asked my gran what she'd like for
Christmas. I'd saved up my pocket money to
buy her something nice.

Child   Some soap?

Narrator   I said.

Child   Pink? Green? To match the bathroom.

Gran   Mmmmmmmm.

14

Narrator   Said Gran, shaking her head.

Gran   Not soap.

Child   What then? Chocolates! Lovely, creamy, sloshy centres. Eat them in front of the telly, watching the Queen.

Gran   Mmmmmmmm.

Narrator   Said Gran, pursing her lips.

Gran   Not chocolates.

Child   I know! Flowers! Roses! Petals red as a holly berry, leaves of green as smooth as silk and thorns sharp like needles pricking your fingers.

Gran   Mmmmmmmm.

Narrator   Said Gran, scratching her chin.

Gran   Not flowers.

Child   (*Thinks. Snaps fingers.*) Slippers! Something warm and cosy. Furry round the top and so comfortable you'll never, ever want to take them off again!

Gran   Mmmmmmmmmm.

Narrator   Said Gran, wrinkling her nose.

Gran   Not slippers.

Child   What then?

Narrator   I said. But before she could answer, the telly went –

T.V.   Ppphhhhhhssssssttttt!

Narrator   Frightening the cat –

Cat   Mieow! Mieow!

16

Narrator	Who leapt into the air, knocking the Christmas tree over –
Xmas tree	(*Percussion*: *crash, bang, tinkling noises.*)
Narrator	And jumped over the back of the sofa then landed on the dog –
Dog	Woof, woof, woof!
Narrator	Then the doorbell rang –
Doorbell	(*Chime bars*) Ding, dong!
Narrator	And –
Milkman	*Milk!*
Narrator	Shouted the milkman just as Grandad careered through from the kitchen singing –

Once in Royal David's city stood a lowly cattle shed...

17

Grandad	***Once in Royal David's City stood . . .*** *(etc.)*
Narrator	At the top of his voice and then my brother hollered down the stairs –
Brother	***Who's got the Sellotape? I want to wrap my presents up!***
Child	***Not me!***
Narrator	I shouted back then Mum yelled –
Mother	***Stop that arguing!***
	(*Noises fade.*)
Narrator	And Gran just looked at me.
Gran	Do you know what I'd really like for Christmas? Only you'd never be able to buy it.
Child	What's that?
Narrator	I said. And Gran replied –
Gran	A bit of peace and quiet!
	(*Noises all start again, count to twenty, stop!*)

Waiting

David Williams

A play with nine characters

The Pupils	*The Staff*
Nicky	Mrs Long
Sarah	Mr Flynn
Scott	Secretary
Kate	Head
Laura	

(*Nicky is standing outside the Head's study.*)

Nicky (*to herself*) What do I do? Have I to knock? What if he's got somebody in there? He won't want me barging in. I'd better wait.

(*Pause. Sarah passes by.*)

Sarah Hi, Nicky. What's up?

Nicky Nothing.

Sarah What you doing here?

Nicky Waiting.

Sarah For the Head?

Nicky Yeah.

Sarah   You in trouble?

Nicky   Dunno.

Sarah   What you been doing?

Nicky   Nothing.

Sarah   It's worse if you don't know.

Nicky   Is it?

Sarah   Yeah. Can't prepare yourself. See ya.

Nicky   Right.

(*To herself*) Can't prepare yourself. What for? What have I done? Dunno.

(*The bell rings.*)

Twenty to four. He said half past three. Should I knock?

(*She knocks very faintly.*)

He can't have heard that. Do I knock again? What if he heard me the first time? What's best to do?

(*Scott comes up behind her.*)

Scott   Hey!

Nicky   Oh! What a shock you gave me!

Scott   Is this a queue?

Nicky   Sort of.

Scott	What time are you in for?
Nicky	Half past.
Scott	He's late, then. I'm not hanging about.
Nicky	Are you wanting to see him?
Scott	Who'd *want* to see him? He said twenty to. Well, I've got papers to deliver. I'm not hanging about.

21

Nicky	You can take my place if you like.
Scott	No way. I'm off. When he comes out tell him I was here. Tell him I was here on the dot. Not my fault if he's late. Got my papers to do. You tell him, right?
Nicky	Well . . .
Scott	See ya.
Nicky	What if . . .
	(*To herself*) He'll take it out on me. Bound to. Double punishment. I don't even know that lad's name.
	(*Calling*) Hey, what's your name? Hey!
	(*Mrs Long comes out of the staffroom.*)
Mrs Long	What are you yelling at?
Nicky	Sorry, Mrs Long.
Mrs Long	Nicola Harvey. What are you doing here?
Nicky	The Head wants to see me.
Mrs Long	Really? Why?
Nicky	I dunno.
Mrs Long	I *don't* know.
Nicky	Me neither, Miss . . . Mrs . . .

Mrs Long	Strange he should want to see you. Does he know who you are?
Nicky	Don't know.
Mrs Long	No. Strange. You're not . . . you're not musical, are you?
Nicky	No.
Mrs Long	I thought not.
	(*Moving away*) Never mind, it'll all come out in the wash.
Nicky	(*To herself*) What will? What will come out in the wash?
Mrs Long	(*Down the corridor*) Don't run, you two. Walk!
	(*Scuffling as Kate and Laura pass by.*)
Kate	Hey, Nicky.
Laura	You messenger today?
Nicky	What?
Laura	Messenger. You know, where you have to take notes about all day. It's a right skive.
Kate	That's just First Years.
Laura	Oh, yeah. So who you waiting for?
Nicky	The Head.

Laura	Ooh!
Kate	What for?
Nicky	Dunno. He wants to see me.
Kate	Did your parents get a letter?
Nicky	Don't think so. He just told Mr Stokes.
Laura	What's it about?
Nicky	Haven't a clue.
Kate	Go on, you must know.
Nicky	Don't.
Laura	It's not about the skeleton, is it?
Nicky	What?
Kate	You know the skeleton from the lab?
Laura	Somebody took it an' sat it on the loo.
Nicky	They didn't!
Laura	You must've heard about it.
Nicky	No. The girls' loo?
Kate	Yeah.
Laura	You must've heard.

Nicky   No. I've been off.

Kate   Skiving off?

Nicky   Off sick.

Kate   Did you bring a note?

Nicky	No. It was only one day.
Laura	You're supposed to bring a note.
Nicky	What, for one day?
Laura	Yeah. It's in the school rules.
Nicky	I didn't know that. I've never been off before. Mr Stokes never said.
Kate	You're supposed to know.
Laura	It says in the rules.
Kate	Wouldn't want to be in your shoes.
Laura	Me neither. See you later, maybe.
Kate	See ya.
Nicky	(*To herself*) I didn't know you had to bring a note. Not for one day.
Kate	(*Echo*) Wouldn't want to be in your shoes.
Nicky	(*To herself*) Oh, no, my shoes! I've got my green ones on. Why did I have to put my green ones on. What will I do now? I've got trainers in my bag.
	(*Unzipping the bag*) Is it worse to be wearing trainers or green shoes? Could say I was at Games. What if he checks? Could say I'm going out jogging. Yes, that's best.

(Nicky starts to change her shoes in the corridor. Mr Flynn comes out of the staffroom.)

Mr Flynn   What do you think you're doing?

Nicky   Mmm, I'm . . . putting my trainers on.

Mr Flynn   What on earth for?

Nicky   Well . . . jogging, sir.

Mr Flynn	What do we have changing rooms for? Get yourself along there.
Nicky	Yes, sir. (*Pause*)
Mr Flynn	Well? I mean now.
Nicky	But . . . but I have to see the Head.
Mr Flynn	He's not going jogging, is he?
Nicky	Don't think so. He wants to see me.
Mr Flynn	Why didn't you say so? Have you knocked?
Nicky	Yes. Well, not hard.
Mr Flynn	I don't know, you people. Can't do the simplest things. (*He knocks on the door and opens it.*) Excuse me . . . Oh, nobody here. What time was he supposed to see you?
Nicky	Half past three.
Mr Flynn	Must have been held up. He's bound to be along in a moment. Sit and wait in there.
Nicky	In there?
Mr Flynn	Yes. Don't want you cluttering up the corridor. And tie up those laces. (*He closes the door, leaving Nicky alone in the Head's study.*)

28

Nicky (*To herself*) I've never been in here before. Where does that other door go? Should I sit back here or beside the desk? He might not like me sitting inside without his say-so. But Mr Flynn'll tell us off if I go out again. Never get the choice, do you? Go here, go there. Do this. And I still don't know what to do about these shoes. What if I sit here and put my bag in front? He maybe won't notice them. Right.

(*Pause*)

That's a big desk, bigger than Mr Stokes' tatty thing. I suppose the higher up you are the bigger desk you get. And posh. Flowers on it an' everything. Telephone. What's that photo?

(*She stands up to inspect it.*)

This must be his family. His wife's quite pretty except for her hair. About the same age as Mam. God, bet my Mam's worrying now. It's well after four. Wonder how long he'll be. Wish I could ring her. It's his fault he's so late, so why shouldn't I use his phone? But what if somebody walks in in the middle of it? Suppose I put the latch on the door, just for a minute.

(*She locks the door.*)

Nicky Just while I ring Mam. Now, then, 9 for Exchange. I don't want that. 0 for Operator. This button says Call.

(*She presses it.*)

Secretary (*On the telephone loudspeaker*) Yes, Mr Todd?

Nicky	Oh!
	(*Nicky drops the photo, which breaks on the desk.*)
Secretary	Are you all right?
	(*Nicky stabs randomly at buttons.*)
	Hello. Hello?
	(*Her voice is cut off as Nicky finds the right button.*)
Nicky	Oh, Mam! What have I done? The photo's smashed. They'll know it's me. Get rid of it. Get rid of it.
	(*As she gathers up the glass there is a knock on the door.*)
Secretary	Mr Todd?
	(*Nicky whimpers. The handle turns but the door is locked.*)
Secretary	Mr Todd? Are you in there?
Nicky	(*To herself*) Hide, hide. Through the other door.
	(*She opens the door.*)
	It's a cupboard. What's this? There's a skeleton . . . a skeleton in the cupboard.
Secretary	(*Outside*) Oh there you are, Mr Todd. Did you call me just now?
Head	(*Outside*) No, I'm just back from County Hall.
Secretary	Funny. Has someone been using your office?

Head	Not that I'm aware . . . Let's see.
	(*He tries the door.*)
	Locked. Hang on.
Nicky	(*To herself*) Oh, help. What's worse, the Head or the skeleton?
	(*The key turns.*)
	Move over.
	(*Nicky hides in the cupboard as the Head and the Secretary enter the room.*)
Head	Come on in, let's see if we can sort this out.
Secretary	There you are. I knew I heard something. Look at this glass.
Head	Broken window?
Secretary	No. It's the photograph from your desk.
Head	What a mean trick. Why would anyone want to do that?
Secretary	Revenge. You've made an enemy.

Head	Scott Morrison!
Secretary	I wouldn't be surprised.
Head	Guaranteed. He was supposed to come and see me tonight . . . again.
Secretary	What for this time?
Head	My spies tell me he's the one responsible for the lab skeleton popping up in unlikely places. I was going to confront him with it tonight.

Secretary	But he hasn't turned up.
Head	He'll have turned up all right. He's found the office empty, broken this picture frame and scarpered. Wait till I see him on Monday.
Secretary	There's someone else in your diary – you're supposed to see Nicola Harvey.
Head	Who? Oh yes, the girl with the story.
Secretary	The one who won the competition?
Head	Mmm, only she doesn't know it yet. I was going to announce it in assembly yesterday, but apparently she was off. So I asked her form teacher to send her along. I'm very keen to congratulate her personally. It was very well-written . . . one of those quirky pieces about someone being locked up overnight in the Chamber of Horrors at Madame Tussaud's. An old idea, of course, but cleverly done.
Secretary	There's no sign of her.
Head	Well, I am very late. It can wait until Monday. You know, I don't see nearly enough of these bright kids. They just slip by unnoticed in the school while toe-rags like Morrison demand all the attention. Ah well, that's life. I'm off. Can I give you a lift anywhere?
Secretary	Thanks. If you wouldn't mind dropping me off at the Post Office . . .

Head   Fine. Hold on, I'll just lock everything up. That bit of vandalism has suddenly made me very security-conscious.

(*He locks his drawers, and the door of the cupboard.*)

That's it. Let's go.

(*Leaving*) Your car's still off the road, then?

(*Nicky knocks from inside the cupboard.*)

Secretary   There's a knocking noise.

Head   Really? Could be the valves.

Secretary   No, I mean now. In your office. Listen.

(*Nicky knocks again.*)

Head   What . . .

Secretary   It's coming from the cupboard.

Head   (*Unlocking the cupboard*) If this is another one of those stupid practical jokes . . .

(*He throws open the door of the cupboard to reveal Nicky standing inside with the skeleton.*)

Nicky   Good evening, sir. I'm Nicola Harvey. I . . . believe you wanted to see me.

The Day the Animals Talked

Terry Jones

A poem for eighteen voices: a narrator and seventeen animals –

Goldfish	**Leopard**
Dog (Rover)	**Mink**
Cat	**Seal**
Budgie	**Bear**
Mouse	**Musk deer**
Goose	**Fox**
Bison	**Crocodile**
Deer	**Elephant**
Lion	

I woke up one morning
When the sun was high,
And I thought: 'Something's up!'
Though I didn't know why.

I got out of bed,
Then I went white as chalk,
For I suddenly heard
My goldfish talk.

'Ah! You've got up at last!
And about time!' it said.
'I've been swimming all night,
While you've been in bed!'

37

Well! You can imagine
My utter surprise;
I didn't believe
My ears or my eyes.

I was going to exclaim:
'Did I hear you talk?'
But just then the dog said:
'I need a walk!'

I turned and saw Rover
(Imagine the shock)
As he said: 'A good long one –
Not once round the block!'

I thought: 'This is crazy!'
But more was to come . . .
When I started to answer,
I found I was dumb!

I spluttered and pointed
And tried to say: 'Wait!'
But nothing came out,
And the cat muttered: 'Great!'

'The Boss has gone mute on us!
Just what we need!
How's he going to buy catfood?'
'And what about seed?'

This was the budgie,
Pacing its cage,
And who all of a sudden
Flew into a rage:

'Lemme out! You sadist!'
It pecked at its bell.
'I can't bear this prison!
My life here is hell!'

I tried to say 'Sorry!'
But nothing came out,
Then it was the goldfish
Who'd started to shout:

'What about me?
I'm stuck in this bowl
With nowhere to hide
Not so much as a hole!

'Don't you think *I* go crazy?
I'm stared at all day
By that monster!' But Ginger
The cat looked away.

And I tried to say: 'Pets!
Please listen to me!'
But I was as dumb
As *they'd* been previously.

'You listen to us,
For a change!' said a mouse
Who appeared on a cupboard
'We live in this house,

'Yet you fill it with traps,
And you poison my young!'
And the others all murmured:
'He ought to be hung!'

But Rover stood by me,
And said: 'Listen here!
It may be the Master
Has just no idea

'Of half of the things
That go on in his name . . .'
The cat said: 'Let's show him!'
The rest said: 'We're game!'

So the animals dragged me
By beak and by paw
To the zoo, and I couldn't
Believe what I saw:

All the cages were open
The creatures roamed free,
And walked on their hind legs
Like you and like me.

When they saw me, they started
To scream: 'One's got loose!'
'That's a dangerous animal!'
Clamoured a goose.

'They've cooked all my ancestors,
Thousands a year!'
'And mine!' cried a bison.
'And mine!' sighed a deer.

And the animals started
To bellow and roar,
Till the lion held up
An immaculate paw:

'Now listen! A lot of us
Hunt for our meat.
This creature's no different.
His kind have to eat.'

'But they torture us, Lion!'
The goose again crowed.
'They force us to feed
Till our livers explode!'

'Is this *possible*, Man?'
The lion turned to me,
And I couldn't deny it
(Nor could I agree).

And the murmur of horror
Turned into a roar,
As the leopard sprang up
And growled: 'I hate him more!

'At least the Man eats
The geese that he kills –
My kind he pursues
For his fashions and frills!'

'That's right!' cried the mink
And the seals and the bears.
'Who wants to be murdered
For something *he* wears?'

'And us, dears!' the musk deer
Were whispering as well.
'We're slaughtered merely
'Cause men like our smell!'

'Ah! My friends! This is nothing!'
The fox had begun,
'Men hunt us poor foxes
Simply for *fun*!'

The babble of voices
Arose to the skies,
And the Lion turned to me
With tears in his eyes.

'Oh, Man!' he said sadly,
'What have you to say?'
And I stood there as dumb
As a bottle of hay.

'Make him into a hand-bag!'
The crocodiles croaked.
'Turn him into a hat-stand,'
The elephants joked.

And the lion said: 'Oh, Man!
How *could* you have done
All these terrible things
By the light of the sun?

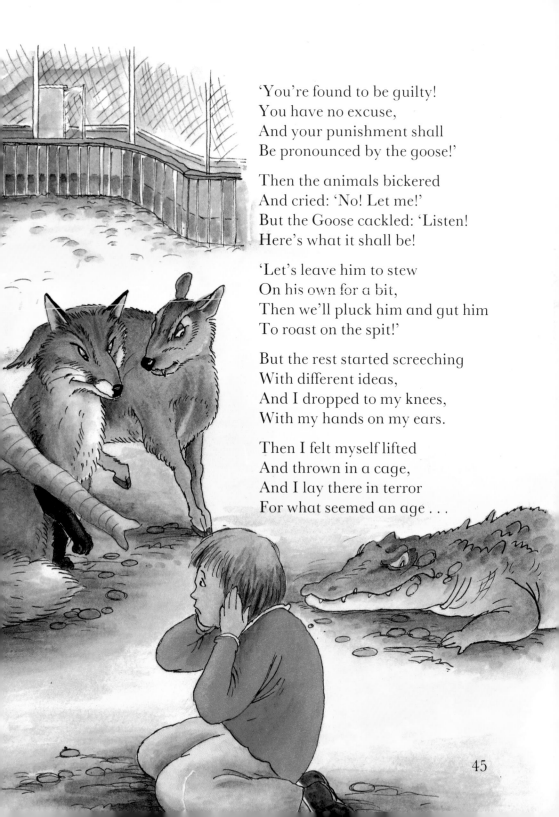

'You're found to be guilty!
You have no excuse,
And your punishment shall
Be pronounced by the goose!'

Then the animals bickered
And cried: 'No! Let me!'
But the Goose cackled: 'Listen!
Here's what it shall be!

'Let's leave him to stew
On his own for a bit,
Then we'll pluck him and gut him
To roast on the spit!'

But the rest started screeching
With different ideas,
And I dropped to my knees,
With my hands on my ears.

Then I felt myself lifted
And thrown in a cage,
And I lay there in terror
For what seemed an age . . .

I awoke all alone.
Above me – the stars –
When I suddenly heard
A quiet tap on the bars,

And there was old Rover
At my cage's doors,
Concern in his eyes
And a key in his jaws.

'Come on, Master,' he grumbled,
'While everyone sleeps,
Let's get out of here
— this place gives me the creeps!'

He opened the cage
And I licked his dear face,
And I kept close to heel,
For I felt in disgrace.

And when we got home,
He put me to bed
Under the table,
And gently he said:

'Goodnight, old fellow,'
In his kindly tone,
And he patted my head,
And he gave me a bone.

And I settled right down,
And I slept like a log,
Thinking: 'Golly! I'm happy
I'm only a dog!'

Acknowledgements

The editor and publisher are grateful for permission to include the following material:

James Berry, 'Sunny Market Song' from *When I Dance* (Hamish Hamilton), © James Berry 1988. Reprinted by permission of the publisher. Tony Bradman, 'The Behaviour Report', © Tony Bradman 1993. Reprinted by permission of Rogers Coleridge & White Ltd. Terry Jones, 'The Day the Animals Talked' from *The Curse of the Vampire's Socks*. Reprinted by permission of Pavilion Books Ltd. We are also grateful for permission to use this as the volume title. Brian Moses, 'Well, What Happened?' Reprinted by permission of the author. David Williams, 'Waiting', © David Williams 1993. Reprinted by permission of the author. Kit Wright, 'My Dad, Your Dad' from *Rabbiting On*. Reprinted by permission of HarperCollins Publishers Ltd. Irene Yates, 'Christmas Present', © Irene Yates 1993. Reprinted by permission of the author.

The illustrations are by: Paul Cox p.19, p.21, p.25, p.27, p.30, pp.32–3, p.35, p.36; Paul Dowling pp.14–15, pp.16–17, p.18; Helen Musselwhite pp.10–11, pp.12–13; Chris Smedley pp.8–9; Martin Ursell cover, p.37, pp.38–9, p.40, p.41, pp.42–3, pp.44–5, pp.46–7; Marc Vyvyan-Jones pp.4–5; Brian Walker pp.6–7